Grandpus Beard

Poems by Joshua Seigal

Dear Hannah
& Sarah,

enjoy!

Josh

Visit
WWW.JOSHUASEIGAL.CO.UK
for lots more exciting info.

Dedicated to all the children
at all the schools I have visited.

Keep smiling!

Joshua Seigal is a poet, performer and workshop leader based in London. He spends his time visiting schools, libraries and festivals around the UK, where he performs his fun, energetic and interactive poetry. Joshua has taken critically-acclaimed children's poetry shows to the Edinburgh Festival Fringe. He owns a funny, fluffy type of dog called a Lhasa Apso, and his favourite food is a type of Jamaican fruit called ackee.

Contents

Don't Go To The Cake Shop

Legs of frog
Tail of rat
Paws of dog
Whiskers of cat
Slime of slug
Shell of snail
Pin of porcupine
Blubber of whale
Beaver's tongue
Lion's mane
Bark from a tree
Goo from the drain
Scales of snake
And beak of puffin –
That's what goes into
A blueberry muffin.

My Grandpa's Beard

It's like a dead otter attached to his chin,
It looks like a furry grey stoat –
It billows and tumbles its way round his face
Going up to his ears
And down past his throat.

I wonder: at night, does it judder to life
As he lies all tucked up in his bed?
Does it tap out a tango and do a back flip?
Does it fight with the hairs
On the top of his head?

Does it sneak from his face and jump down to
  the floor
And curl under the bed like a cat?
Does it sprout a malevolent pair of wings?
Does it swoop round the room
Like a woolly grey bat?

I shudder to think of the hairs in his sink –
I doubt he'd have need of a plug.
He should gather it up and then he could cash in
And sell all the hairs
To turn into a rug.

For my grandpa's beard's a sight to behold
As it dangles half way down his sweater.
Some say it's the greatest that ever was grown...

But I think my grandma's is better.

On The Menu

Theo says his dad eats humans
He ate the Johnsons and the Newmans

He wolfed the Wolffs and fried the Foxes
He slurped the Smiths and nibbled the Knoxes

He cooked the Cooksons' brains in oil
And roasted the Richards' in silver foil

He attacked the Ahmeds with ravenous glee
And gobbled the Greens with grapes and brie

He boiled the Baileys and potted the Potters
He chopped up the Changs in a bowl of pigs'
  trotters

He goes hunting for Hunters like he's hunting
  for grouse
And we've been invited to Theo's house.

Haircut

When mum gets scissors from their case
My heart goes wild and starts to race

I sit down on a kitchen chair
She starts to tinker with my hair

Hacking at my silky mane
She thinks it is some kind of game –

She's never had one day of training
But her vigour can't be reined in.

Giggling as she nicks my ear
She says I have nothing to fear

She snips away so recklessly
I fear for my sanity

She seems to think it is a hoot!
Then she'll reveal her labour's fruit:

A haircut that she thinks is funky.
But I look more like a monkey.

Leaning on the window sill
She smiles at her self-taught skill;

Her new book *really* worries me –
Beginner's Guide To Dentistry.

The Naughty Chair

If you look in the corner
Jim's sat over there
With his face to the wall,
On The Naughty Chair.
Over there in the corner
Is where Jim's sat,
For he weed on the carpet
And blamed the cat.

It was a good story,
You can't fault him for trying,
But his parents discovered
That Jim had been lying:
His scandalous tale
Fell rather flat -
Jim's family don't
Even own a cat.

Richard Bennett

Richard Bennett's a boy at my school
He hits me, kicks me, calls me a fool
He stomps on my shoes and he yanks my hair
And he chucks my schoolbooks everywhere.
I say to him "I'll tell the teacher"
He says "if you do, I'll beat yer!"
He steals my money and he calls me names
He doesn't let me join in with his games
He puts frogs in my bag and dirt in my food
He flicks my ears, he's incredibly rude.
He pinches my nose and he laughs in my face
He says I am a big disgrace
When I tell him to "stop it, please"
He punches my arms and he kicks my knees.
Richard Bennett's a boy at my school
He hits me, kicks me, calls me a fool
When I get home I tell my mother
And she says
            "Richard, be nice to your brother!"

Copycat

Benny Bratt
Is a copycat.
He looks over my shoulder
Like a slimy little rat,
Scribbling down my answers
In his grubby little book,
Thieving my ideas
Like a loathsome
Little crook.

Benny Bratt
Is a copycat:
As irritating as a wasp
As pesky as a gnat,
But when we have to take a test
I know he will not pass –
I wonder if he knows
That I'm the bottom
Of the class...

Animal House

(This poem features genuine collective nouns)

There's an **ARMY** of **HERRINGS** in my bath
And a **BEVY** of **OTTERS** too
There's a **BOOGLE** of **WEASELS**
Under my easel
And an **IMPLAUSIBILITY** of **GNUS**.

There's a **LAMENTATION** of **SWANS**
And a **MURMERATION** of **STARLINGS**
And a **MURDER** of **CROWS**
In my sink.
There's a **FLAMBOYANCE** of **FLAMINGOS**
In my underwear drawer,
Which is rather odd, I think!

There's a **PARCEL** of **PENGUINS** in my fridge
And a **SHIVER** of **SHARKS** in my bowl,
There's a **MOB** of **MEERKATS** under the rug
Along with a **LABOUR** of **MOLES**.

There's a **PARLIAMENT** of **OWLS**
And a **PANDEMONIUM** of **PARROTS**
And a **KNOB** of **TOADS**
On my pillow,
And in my boxes
There's **SKULK** of **FOXES**
And a **HOOVER** of **ARMADILLOS**.

Lying in my bed
So still they're almost dead
There's a **LAZINESS** of **SLOTHS**,
And if you open up my shed
They'll be flying round your head –
A **UNIVERSE** of **MOTHS**!

I've a **BIKE** of **WASPS** in my trousers,
Nibbling at my bottom,
While a **COALITION** of **CHEETAHS**
Chase a **DAZZLE** of **ZEBRAS**
Down the hall – I think they got 'em!
And into my toilet I dare not go –
There's an **OBSTINACY** of **BUFFALO**...

A **COMMITTEE** of **VULTURES** circles the ceiling
And if you want to know how I'm really feeling,
Well, I like my varied company
But the thing I *most* like to do
Is to go down the road
And to look at the **CROWD** of **HUMANS**
In the zoo!

Wishing On A Star

(Written for Whitmore Primary School on National Poetry Day 2012)

I wish, shooting star,
for a ten ton chocolate bar,
and a crisp packet with an infinite
number of crisps.

I wish my team would never lose
a match, and that, whenever dad
threw me the ball, I would never
drop a catch.

I wish that cartoons were on TV
for 24 hours a day, and that there
was no such thing as school,
so we could stay in
and watch those cartoons.

I wish that, instead of going
to Spain, or Devon, we could
go on holiday to the moon,
and that the government
could see sense, and *finally* make
a law banning broccoli.

I wish there was
a world-championship for scrambling
up trees, and for my bed-time
to be half-past-three
in the morning, and that maths
didn't have to be
so boring.

I wish, shooting star, for you
to get this letter.

But most of all,
shooting star,
I wish for grandma
to get better.

BEE IN THE CLASSROOM!

The sun shines bright, and through the trees
We hear the whisper of a breeze,
The sparrows sing their summer song –
Let's open the window! What can go wrong?...

... BEE IN THE CLASSROOM!
BEE IN THE CLASSROOM!
Panic! Chaos! What a fuss!

BEE IN THE CLASSROOM!
BEE IN THE CLASSROOM!
Dive down quick! It's after us!

BEE IN THE CLASSROOM!
BEE IN THE CLASSROOM!
Jump up screaming in the air!

BEE IN THE CLASSROOM!
BEE IN THE CLASSROOM!
Hide behind the teacher's chair!

It's big and furry, black and yellow,
We go wild and start to bellow
BEE IN THE CLASSROOM – can't ignore it
BEE IN THE CLASSROOM – try to floor it:
Lash at it with rolled up notebook!
Poke at it with a broken coat hook!

BEE IN THE CLASSROOM!
BEE IN THE CLASSROOM!
Pout at it! Shout at it!
Stick your tongue out at it!

BEE IN THE CLASSROOM!
BEE IN THE CLASSROOM!
Hack at it! whack at it!
Throw your rucksack at it!

Do our work? A crazy notion!
BEE IN THE CLASSROOM – what a commotion

Writing today
Is a total write-off
Given the creature
That we've caught sight of;
My favourite time to
Be in the classroom
Is when there is a
BEE IN THE CLASSROOM!

Fun and Games

James scraped his elbow and Jack hurt his nose;
Sarah and Abigail, they came to blows.

Alex screamed out as he rolled round in pain
And Emma sulked off in the corner again.

Craig and Takashi, they got in a fight;
Finn couldn't stop laughing, try as he might.

Olga is claiming her leg has been broken;
Bella is squeezing and Poppy is choking.

So enough of the madness! Enough of the menace!
That's the last time we all play table tennis!

Bad Day

Michael is rampaging
through the classroom, overturning chairs,
lashing out at whoever gets in his way.

Today is one of his Bad Days.

They say he might be leaving this school;
when the teacher suggested it to his mum
she said it would be 'for the best'.
The other children test him,
see how far they can push him
before he snaps and screams
SHUT UP! SHUT UP!,
sending the class
into giggling fits.

When the class are working
Michael just sits.
Sometimes one of the other kids
tries to catch his eye,
causing Michael to fly
into a wild rage

And today is one of his Bad Days.
The bear has escaped its cage:
Michael piles into them
with windmilling fists,
sending a girl's head
crashing against a desk.

Yes today is a Bad Day.
The headmaster calls Michael's mum,
who comes to take him home.

I can see Michael and his mum
through the window now,
cuddling close together as they walk
across the car-park, towards the car.
It's the only time I've ever
seen him smiling.

Team Earth

(Written for Kingsgate Primary School for Friendship Week)

My Uncle Graham
believes in aliens.
I used to think he was stupid
but I don't anymore –

Think of sport:
every few years,
during the World Cup,
we forget the teams
we usually support
and start cheering whole countries,
with their players
brought together
from lots of different teams.

But wouldn't it be better
if the world *itself*
could form a team,
made up of players
from different countries,
cultures, colours and creeds?

You might say there'd be no one
for this team to play against.
But what if there were aliens?
If there were aliens
the world would have to unite,
arm in arm for the Great
Intergalactic
Penalty Shootout.

So now I think
I like the thought
that Uncle Graham's right.
I like the thought
that the stars
we see at night
harbour aliens,
bringing us together.

Let's Hear It For Teachers

Let's hear it for teachers,
A curious crew.
There isn't a limit
To what they will do –

They mark all your work
And they do not despair
When you *still* cannot tell
Between 'there', 'their' and 'they're'.

They tell you the same thing
Again and again
While you sit staring blankly
And chewing your pen.

Sometimes their job
Isn't terribly fun,
With scary inspectors
And scarier mums,

And screaming young children
And meddling MPs
Picking holes in their work
Like a lump of Swiss cheese.

But listen to me
For I swear that it's true:
The reason they teach is
They care about you.

The reason they get up
At stupid o'clock
Is to give you the key
That will open the lock.

They're desperate to help you
To be at your best,
To be better people
(Not just pass a test),

To do well, to think well
And walk tall with pride.
Let's hear it for teachers,
For ~~there~~ ~~their~~ they're on your side.

I'm Sorry

I'm sorry that I hit you
I'm sorry that I laughed
I'm sorry that I said you had
A neck like a giraffe.

I'm sorry that I spat at you
I'm sorry that I kicked you
I'm sorry that I told on you
I'm sorry that I tricked you.

I'm sorry that I took your lunch
And made fun of your cat
I'm sorry that I said I'd rather
Be friends with a rat.

I'm sorry that I tickled you
And sent you nasty texts
I'm sorry that I stole your coat
And that I hid your specs.

I'm sorry that I didn't stop
When you said "that's enough"
I'm sorry that I picked a fight
And tried to look all tough.

I'm sorry that I did all this.
I didn't mean to spite you,
I only did these things
Because
    in fact
        I really like you –

I'm sorry for the things I did,
I know it's strange to mention
That I only did these things
So you'd give me attention.

So I hope that you'll forgive me
And this poem's made you see
That I'm *really* sorry...
...Will you go out with me
    Miss?

My Sister Has A Boyfriend

My sister has a boyfriend
She can't stand to be without him
My sister has a boyfriend
And I know all about him:

He supports Tottenham Hotspur
And he plays the bass guitar,
He's saving all his money up
So he can buy a car.

The other week he had a fight
With a guy called Brian,
He isn't doing well at school
Even though he's trying.

His eyes are blue and beautiful
He has a rugged jaw,
He doesn't like cooked cauliflower
But he'll eat it raw.

One day he plans to leave this place
And sail round the world,
He wants to take my sister with
Because she is 'his girl'.

My sister has a boyfriend
She can't stand to be without him
My sister has a boyfriend
And I know all about him:

OK, I don't know *everything* –
I've not met him at all –
But when my sister's on the phone
I listen through the wall.

Going Bald

My dad's going bald. On the top of his head
There used to be hair – now it's shiny instead.
I say that I love him and that I don't care,
But dad says he's nothing bereft of his hair.
He's got all these lotions and potions and mousses
And bottles of oil and strange coloured juices
Which he smears daily all over his dome –
He rubs it all in but the hairs just won't come.
His bonce remains gleaming and squeaky and pink
So he goes to the cupboard and takes out the ink –
He pours it quite liberally over his cranium
Then he goes out and he picks a geranium.
Squashing the petals he rubs them all in
Then he opens up bottles of vodka and gin
And he tips out the contents onto the bald patch,
But still he can't seem to recover his thatch
So he goes to the garden and digs up some ants
and he says to himself "maybe this is my chance!"
He boils them up in a big bowl of broth
And he soaks it all up with a big piece of cloth
And he dabs and he prods and he rubs but, oh no!
His head is still bald and the hairs still won't grow...
I wish he'd give up and mop up with some tissues –
I think a bald head is the least of his issues.

Dog Haiku

Woof woof growl yap growl
Growl snarl woof woof yap woof snarl
Howl growl snarl woof woof

Parrot Poem

Parrot poem.

Parrot poem.

Parrot poem.

Who Cares?

I'm a real man.
My hands are so strong
They'll crush your skull like a vice,
My biceps are rippling
And my frown is not nice,
A gallon of beer is my favourite drink
And my favourite colour
Is pink.

I like boxing
And football
And driving fast cars,
I spend my evenings
Having fights in bars,
I don't have girlie baths, I just wash
In the sink,
And my favourite colour
Is pink.

You might say it's silly
But I say 'who cares?'
My walls are pink, and my posters
And stickers,
And under my trousers
I wear frilly pink knickers.

'Cos I'm a real man, I don't care
What you think,
And my favourite colour
IS PINK!

Before Long

We put a lion and a tiger in a den together –
Before long we got a liger.

We put a whale and a dolphin in a pool together –
Before long we got a wolphin.

We put a zebra and a horse in a field together –
Before long we got a zorse.

We put a crocodile and an alligator in a swamp
  together –
Before long we got a crocogator.

We put mum and dad in a room together –
Before long we got mad.

Bradley

(Written for Harvey Road Primary School,
whose Year 2 class have a pet stick insect)

In Year 2 we have a pet –
Bradley is his name.
Bradley is a stick insect
And Bradley has a game:
He often likes to leave his box
And crawl across the floor,
He'll rest upon the window sill
Or linger by the door.

He likes to lurk among the books
And wallow in the sink,
He sometimes nibbles at our lunch
And drinks our teacher's drink!
He lolls across the radiator
Basking in the heat,
And when we're sitting at our desks
He'll flit across our feet.

In Year 2 we have a pet –
Bradley is his name.
Bradley is a stick insect
And Bradley has a game:

He hides in teacher's handbag
And he gives her such a fright
That she leaps up high into the air
And screams with all her might!

She says that Bradley's escapades
Are making her feel sick
So she went into the playground
And she came back with a stick.
She put the stick in Bradley's box
And told him "This is Brian.
He is your new insect pal –
Now you play Sleeping Lions!"

The Goldfish Gobbler

I'm a Goldfish Gobbler,
My favourite dish
Is a juicy young
Slimy young
Oily young fish.

I sneak into your house
And I prowl through your kitchen,
I see your little fishy
And my skin
Begins itching.

My nose starts twitching!
The fish looks yummy!
I've a rumbling
Grumbling
Tumbling tummy.

I'm a Goldfish Gobbler,
My fangs are like spears,
My eyes burn like coals
And my claws
Are like shears.

I clamber on the table
And I gaze into the bowl,
I scoop up little fishy
And I gobble
Him whole,

And all the fishy parents
Tell stories of me,
Of the goldfish-gobbling goblin
Eating fishes
For its tea!

'Cos I'm a Goldfish Gobbler –
On fishes I grow fat,
I'm a Goldfish Gobbler
And I'll also eat a rat,
Yes I'm a Goldfish Gobbler,
Though some just call me

'Cat!'

Henrietta the Eighth

What would I do if I were queen?
I'd be evil, I'd be mean.
I'd take six husbands
Then, one by one,
Annihilate them
Just for fun.

I'd take the first
And mince his brain
Then throw him
Underneath a train.
I'd feed the second
To poisonous snakes
And scoop up what's left
With a garden rake.

I'd stone the third to death
With cheese
And drown the fourth
In a bath of peas.
The fifth I'd bludgeon
With a trowel
Then I'd smother the sixth
With a kitchen towel.

What would I do if I were queen?
I'd be evil, I'd be mean.
At first I'd get
Some dirty looks,
Then you'd read about *me*
In the history books.

Zombie Poem

What's slushy and what's mushy
And so very good to eat?
What's wobbly and knobbly
And is a tasty treat?
What is it that I dream of
When I'm shambling down the street?
It's brains brains brains brains
BRRRRRAINS !

What is that goo that's greyish-blue,
That thing I love to munch?
What is it that I slurp on
When I sit down to my lunch?
What has a soggy texture
Blended with a pleasant crunch?
It's brains brains brains brains
BRRRRRAINS !

What is that thing that gives you life
And lives inside your head?
What is it that I'll nick from you
As you lie in your bed?
What are those tasty morsels
That I need to keep me fed?
They're brains brains brains brains
BRRRRRAINS!

What is it that your teacher has
That makes her very smart?
What makes her good at languages
And history and art?
What is it that'll I'll gobble up
Before the lesson starts?
Her brains brains brains brains
BRRRRRAINS!

But chewing them is tiring
And I need some time to play.
I need some relaxation
Yes I need to get away.
Where is it that I'll travel to
For my holiday?

It's Spain Spain Spain Spain
SPPPAAAIINNN!!!

Ooshus Magooshus

Ooshus Magooshus
Lives under the stairs
You shouldn't disturb him
You wouldn't dare –
He'll claw at your face
And he'll tear at your hair,
For this is Ooshus
Magooshus's lair.

Ooshus Magooshus
Lives out in the shed
You shouldn't disturb him
He'll have you for dead,
But he comes out at night
(I've heard it said)
To feast on children
In their beds.

Ooshus Magooshus
Lives up in the loft
He likes his bones crunchy
He likes his flesh soft,
He feasted last week
He scoffed and scoffed
And he let out a burp –
You can still smell the waft.

Now Ooshus Magooshus,
He sometimes goes out
He wanders the street
He wanders about
So if you pass a stranger
And you are in doubt
Scream 'OOSHUS MAGOOSHUS!'
With a big, hefty shout!

Clowns Are Evil

(Get into two groups. One group repeats the chorus while the other group recites the poem all the way through.)

Clowns are evil
Clowns are bad
Clowns make me angry
Clowns make me mad.

They're the most annoying creatures
In the whole human race
With all that silly powder
Smeared on their face,
With stupid checkered trousers
And big flappy shoes
I want to punch them on the nose
And give them a bruise

Because clowns are evil
Clowns are bad
Clowns make me angry
Clowns make me mad.

I hate those silly wigs they wear
They make me want to cry
I want to splat them in the face
With a custard pie,
They are about as funny
As a baby's dirty nappy
They do not make me laugh
And they do not make me happy

Because Clowns are evil
Clowns are bad
Clowns make me angry
Clowns make me mad.

So if you have a party
Let me say to you:
You can have a magician
You can go to the zoo
You can serve up lovely jelly
That was made by your mum,
But if there is a clown there
I WILL NOT COME!

Because clowns are evil
Clowns are bad
Clowns make me angry
Clowns make me mad.

Yes clowns are EVIL!
Clowns are BAD!
Clowns make me ANGRY!
Clowns make me MAD!

The Unfortunate Story of Lenny

Lenny had a terrible problem.
He couldn't tell anyone about it.

Every day in school, when his eyes wandered
from the blackboard, his teacher would address
  him in harsh tones:
  Lenny! What's the matter?
  Why aren't you concentrating?
But Lenny never told the truth.

When he got home he would fling his rucksack
into a corner and go up to his room and sit
on his bed. His mum would come in and ask him
  softly,
  Lenny, how was school?
  How was your day?
But Lenny would never answer.

He'd stay in his room all evening, only agreeing
to eat his supper if it was quickly dispatched
  through the door.
He never came down to sit with the family.

Lenny had a terrible problem,
and nobody knew what it was.
He couldn't even tell the posters on the wall
and he never wrote it down in words.
He never told his friends because
he never expected them to care.

Lenny sits in the dolls' house,
old and frayed, slumped
against the tiny desk.
If he could talk
I wonder what he'd say.

For Elise

*(Inspired by Beethoven's 'Für Elise',
my favourite piece of music ever)*

Elise, my love, you mean the world,
The sun and moon to me,
Your eyes are pools of distant stars,
Your hair it is the sea.

Elise, my love, I'd gladly give
The ocean and the shore
And all the pebbles on the beach
To see your face once more.

Your breath is the beat of a butterfly's wing
Tumbling in the breeze;
When the wind whistles through the woods
It whispers your name – Elise.

And now, Elise, you've gone away –
A distant flow of water.
If only I could change the past
My darling girl, my daughter.

The Ferocious Commotion

A ferocious commotion's occurring next door
It's like ten thousand buffalo having a fight
It's as loud as the crash of a rusty chainsaw
And I know it'll keep me awake half the night.

Like the whistling whoosh of a runaway train
A ferocious commotion's occurring next door
Like a hideous gargoyle yelling in pain
It's as loud as a battlefield, loud as a war.

It roars like a lion that's stepped on a pin
It clanks like a tank that's got stuck in the mud
It shrieks like a shark when you tickle its fin
With a hoot and a honk and a bang and a thud.

What on earth is it? I go exploring
And discover it's only my grandfather snoring.

Multicoloured Socks

If you feel ill
If you have chicken-pox
Put a smile on your face –
Wear multicoloured socks.

If you're being bullied
If they hit you with rocks
You'll feel much better
Wearing multicoloured socks.

If you feel sad
If you feel blue
You must listen to me,
Here's what you do:
You reach under your bed
And you pull out a box
And you open it up
And you take out the socks.
You'll feel mighty fine
With these socks on your feet
And you'll smile
      And you'll smirk
            As you strut
                  Down the street.

Nothing can hurt you
Or give you a shock
(Not even a giant, runaway ox)
When you're wearing your special
Multicoloured socks.

Do Me A Favour

I offered to cook my mum breakfast
I asked her what she'd like
I was shocked by the answer she gave me
But I dashed away on my bike.

I pedalled for miles and miles
Through rain and through sleet and through hail,
I had to fulfil my mission!
I knew I must not fail!

I reached the outskirts of Cardiff
Round about half past eight
With my air-pistol in my pocket
I lay in a garden to wait.

I saw a creature moving
And leaping about on the lawn,
I had to get it quickly!
I had to be home at dawn!

I took the gun from my pocket
I had the poor thing in my sights
I shot it and stuffed it in my bag
Then pedalled back home through the night.

I arrived at my house in the morning
And slowly I opened the door
I showed my mum what I'd brought her
And she fainted right there on the floor.

My mum thinks my renegade antics
Are getting to be a bad habit
But I was only trying to help –
She said that she wanted Welsh Rabbit.

All Growed Up

I do not want your kisses
And do not try to hug me
Please don't pinch me on the cheeks
You know it really bugs me.

I won't go with you to the zoo
And don't send me on playdates
I will not run around at break
With my silly schoolmates.

I won't be playing on the swings
I will not skip and hop
I'll be chilling in the pub
Or at the betting shop.

From now on I don't want a pram
I want a nice new car
And I do not want a dummy,
I want a fat cigar.

So take away those cuddly toys –
I do not want to play –
And pour me out a pint of beer:
I'm six years old today.

Breakfast

What do you do when you get out of bed
And you have a dry throat and you have a
 sore head
And you feel like one of the living dead?
Have breakfast.

It's a plate of fuel for the rest of your day
It's a bowl of power for work, rest and play
You wouldn't have it any other way –
It's breakfast.

If you don't eat it you'll feel all grouchy
You'll feel all shuffly, you'll feel all slouchy
So shovel it in your little pouchy –
Have breakfast.

It's porridge! It's toast! It's a blueberry muffin!
I'll tell you one thing and I'll tell you for nothin' –
Your belly is empty, you need to get stuffin'!
No more huffin'!
No more puffin'!
(Although they do eat puffin in Greenland...)
HAVE BREAKFAST!

*(This poem is brought to you by
the National Breakfast Association)*

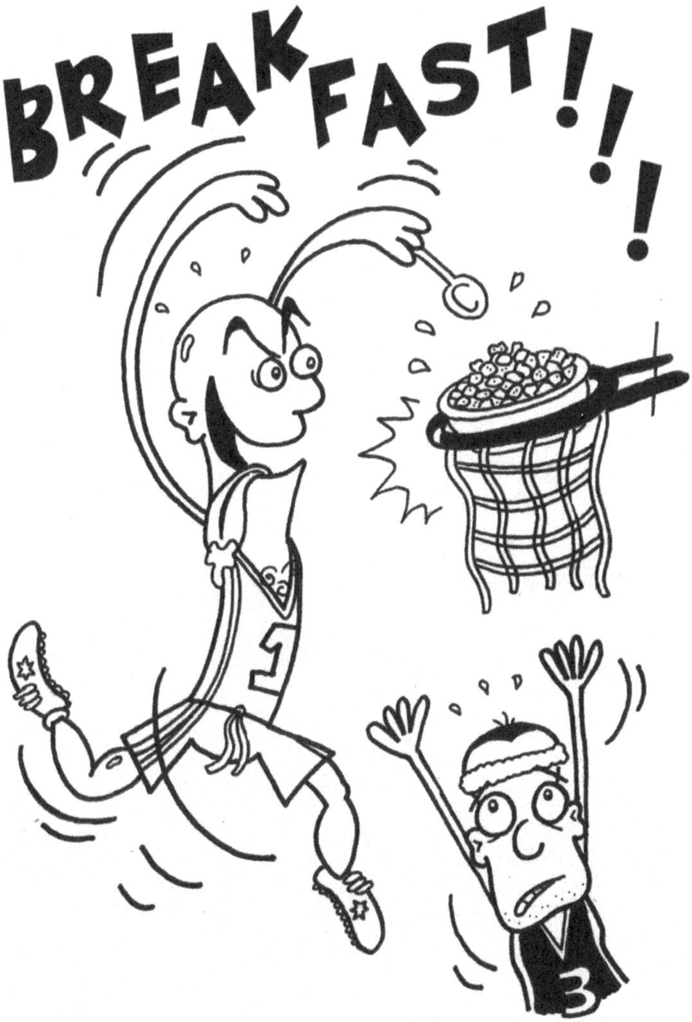
BREAKFAST!!!

Jumble Sale

I've got a toy car I do not need,
I've got so many things it's not funny.
Can I sell them, Mummy, please?
I really need the money.

I've got silly little soldiers
And stupid little teddies,
I want to sell them all, you see
I really think I'm ready.

I've got loads of books I do not read
And lots of horrid videos,
I want to sell them, along with
The games for my Nintendo.

I've got rubber wrestlers I don't really like,
I think I'll sell them along with my bike
And my football stickers can take a hike
Along with my Batman costume.

I'll sell my yo-yo, my playdough, my
  sticklebricks,
My guitar and my box of tricks
And that broken airplane I can't fix
Along with my witch's broom.

I'll sell my xylophone and my Barbie doll
I really don't think I'll miss her,
But really, Mummy, I ask of you:
Can I sell my sister?

Lost

I'm in the supermarket
And recoil with alarm
As I realise my hand has detached
From my mother's arm.
My head is spinning wildly
My eyes are darting round
I'm looking down the aisles
And she's nowhere to be found!
I look in the veggie section
And among the frozen goods
I survey the meat counter
And I scrutinise the puds.
I peer among confectionary
She's very much still missing
So I look among the sausages
The liver and the chicken.
I open the crisp packets
And I glance between the drinks
But she isn't there, or anywhere,
So I sit down and think:
It seems that I am lost for good
At least, that is my hunch
But as long as I am stuck in here
I think I'll have my lunch!

Man Vs Food

The hottest stew, the biggest steak
The largest pizza you can make
A breakfast made with twenty eggs
A bowl of spicy chicken legs
Six litres of the strongest beer –
He'll do it all, he has no fear!

The hugest ever apple pie
He doesn't even need to try
Nine dozen oysters from their shells
Ghost chillies from the depths of hell
A jumbo plate of spicy rib –
All he needs is one clean bib!

Meals made of twenty courses
Burgers made from dogs and horses –
He's the champ, he is the best
But this man needs a proper test,
A dish to make him squirm and cower:
My mum's boiled cauliflower.

Sleepover

We can't eat our meals watching telly,
We can't wear our shoes indoors,
The dog mustn't sleep in our bedroom,
And we'd have to fold our clothes in drawers.

We can't play around in the garden,
Or slide in our socks on the floors,
We'd have to spend our time washing dishes,
And doing lots of other boring chores.

This is how things are in our house,
And we wouldn't want to go against the laws –
I *do* think a sleepover's a good idea,
But please: can we stay at yours?

Muppet!

(A call and response poem)

I forgot to tape my favourite show
Didn't finish the milk in my cereal bowl
Only wore a thin t-shirt when it was cold
What am I?
YOU'RE A MUPPET!

I got ink stains on my brand new fleece
Walked down the road and got chased by geese
Had a chocolate and dropped the very last piece
What am I?
YOU'RE A MUPPET!

I put my pants on the wrong way round
Tried to burp really quietly but did it too loud
Came last in the test and feeling quite proud
What am I?
YOU'RE A MUPPET!

I went swimming in my sister's bikini
Dropped crumbs in my uncle's Lambourghini
Took too many sips from my mum's martini
What am I?
YOU'RE A MUPPET!

I swapped my dog for a packet of crisps
Retook a penalty and I still missed
Drive my teachers round the twist
What am I?
YOU'RE A MUPPET!

So I wrote this poem to keep me in line
Got to the end, tried to think of a rhyme
But couldn't think of what to say...

...What am I?
YOU'RE A MUPPET!!!

John The Jerk

In our class there are sixteen Johns
We try to make things work,
We give each other nicknames –
They call me John The Jerk.

There's John The Big and John The Small,
John Greek and Johnny Turk;
There's Jonathan Tosh
Who's frightfully posh,
And I am John The Jerk.

John The Juggler entertains
While Mean John Jacknife lurks,
There's Siamese triplets,
JohnJohnJohn,
But I'm just John The Jerk.

John The Genius gets full marks
And John The Joker smirks;
There's a boy called
Johhnn!
with a very loud voice,
And little John The Jerk.

Johnny Cash is very rich,
His daddy drives a Merc;
There's a boy who's built backwards
Whose name is Nhoj,
And me – I'm John The Jerk.

And does this make me angry?
I want to go berserk,
But what am I supposed to do?
For I'm just John The Jerk.

Sillius Billius &
Howardus Cowardus

(A poem in two voices)

I'm Roman Emperor Billy McGee
There's no other emperor braver than me
Holding a broom, crouched behind the settee
With a pot on my head, as smart as can be.

I'm Roman Emperor Billy McGee
I live in my palace up there in that tree
This big plastic sword is in my armoury
And here is my horse (OK, it's a doggie).

I'm Roman Emperor Billy McGee
You'll never match up to my greatness, you see
But I *do* require a deputy –
You can take over while I have a wee.

....

*I'm Deputy Emperor Howard McGrew
There's one thing for certain I know to be true
Whatever I say and whatever I do
I'll never match up to the greatness of you.*

*I'm Deputy Emperor Howard McGrew
I'm more out of place than a cat that goes 'moo'
I'm always the last, at the back of the queue
My powerful status feels weird and new.*

*I'm Deputy Emperor Howard McGrew
I don't want to get in a state or a stew
But when you're away there's not much I can do
For you need a wee and, well, I need a poo...*

Tony The One-Trick Pony

I'm a one-trick pony
My name is Tony
My eyes are too bulgy
My legs are too bony

My hooves are too clumpy
My back is all lumpy
My face is too ugly
My mood is too grumpy.

I'm a one-trick pony
My voice is all groany
Nobody likes me
My friends are all phoney

I'm squat and I'm little
My hair is all brittle
Round my nose I have snot
Round my mouth I have spittle.

My teeth are all blunted
My growth is all stunted
When I say 'hi' to people
They look all affronted.

I'm a one-trick pony
I'm hopelessly lonely
I've got the charisma
Of a lump of baloney

My breath is all smelly
I've a sticky-out belly
I never go out
I just stay in watching telly.

My ears are all pointed
My nose is disjointed
My mum is all angry
My dad's disappointed.

My only trick is this, of course:
I can turn myself into...

A BEAUTIFUL HORSE!

Rhymin' Simon

He perched the bread on his head
He scooped up the steak with a rake
He plonked the beans in his jeans
He put the peas on his knees (with the cheese)
He ate the apple in chapel
He chucked the brie in the sea
He fed the mousse to his goose
He ate the mozzarella in the cellar
He flicked the grape at an ape
He served the fish on a dish
He dangled the noodle in front of a poodle
He bought the honey with his money
He gobbled the Marmite under the starlight
He scoffed the mango whilst doing a tango
He threw the berry at a ferry
But he couldn't, just *couldn't*
Work out what to do with the orange...

Fruity World!

If money was honey we'd have sticky pockets
If plugs were rugs we'd need bigger sockets

If a house was a mouse we'd need smaller doors
If judges were budgies we'd have stranger laws

If lizards were wizards the zoo would be freaky
If metals were petals the tap would be leaky

If the gutter was butter the road would be runny
If monks were drunks then prayers would be funny

If cogs were dogs machines would be cute
If apes were grapes we'd be descended from fruit.

Goo

I don't mind **gunk**
I don't mind **slush**
I don't mind **gunge**
I don't mind **mush**
I don't mind **filth**
I don't mind **slime**
I don't mind **sludge**
I don't mind **grime**
I don't mind **gloop**
I don't mind **muck**
I don't mind **ooze**
I don't mind **yuck** –
These things are fine,
But this is true:
You just can't beat
A bit of **GOO!**

Dreams

The blue sky dreams of fluffy clouds
The prisoner dreams of an open door
The footballer dreams of cheering crowds
The soldier dreams of an end to war
The snake dreams of flying like a flock of birds
The bird dreams of burrowing like a mole
The book dreams of being more than words
The broken man dreams of becoming whole
The insomniac dreams of having dreams
The dreamer dreams of being awake
The battlefield dreams of an end to the screams
The birthday girl dreams of her birthday cake
The follower dreams of leading the pack
One dreams of becoming two
Going up the hill, Jill dreams of Jack
And me, I dream of you.

Not A Planet Anymore

*(In 2006, scientists declared that Pluto
should no longer be called a planet)*

All my life I've felt left out –
A tiny speck so far away.
The bigger kids won't let me play,
And now they say they have their doubt

That I am even one of them.
They are big and brave and bold
And I am tiny, blue and cold;
They are wondrous, shiny gems

And they don't want the likes of me.
They all have their moons and things;
Saturn has her lovely rings
And planet Earth has azure seas.

Yes, all my life I've felt left out.
My heart is big, my body small
And all my life I've longed to call:

¡ AM PLUTO!
HEAR
MY
SHOUT!

The Most Embarrassing Moment Ever

The most embarrassing moment ever
was at the beach
I ran up to my mum
wrapped my arms around her legs
and cuddled her tight shouting
mummy! mummy!
but then I looked into the distance
and saw my mum
and my dad
and my sister
and they were pointing at me
and giggling
and the lady I'd been cuddling
starting laughing too and said
"I think you've got the wrong lady"
and I wanted the sea
to wash over me
like a little sandcastle
like a shallow rockpool
and I decided
that I'd never
cuddle anyone again.

Conversation With Bella, Age 3

She tells me her grandpa took leave on a flight
He hopped on a train, he left in the night
He pedalled a bike to a magical place
He's visiting friends in outer space.

She's tells me her grandpa has gone
  somewhere new
He followed the trail to Timbuktu
He's surfing a satellite, circling the stars
He stopped off on Venus, Uranus and Mars.

She tells me her grandpa has gone far away
He packed up his bags for a long holiday
He got in a cab that was bound for the shore
And a rocket conveyed him away with a roar.

She tells me her grandpa is lounging on clouds
He's up in a hammock away from the crowds
And the rocket, it left him – away it sped.
When she grows up she'll tell me
Her grandpa is dead.

My Mum Is In Love
With A Hideous Beast

My mum is in love with a hideous beast
It only comes over at night;
When I'm under my covers
I hear the two lovers
Kissing away out of sight.

My mum is in love with a terrible troll
Or perhaps it is some kind of ghoul;
Round about ten o'clock
I hear keys in the lock
But it's gone when I wake up for school.

I find little love letters all round the flat
And strange little notes on the wall –
The beast calls her 'honey'
And 'darling sweet bunny',
I don't like this creature at all...

Why isn't mum scared out of her wits?
Why doesn't she wail and yell?
If it came in *my* room
I'd grab a big broom
And I'd bludgeon its brains to hell!

So I asked my mum about the beast
She said there's no need to get mad;
She said I was foolish,
The creature's not ghoulish –
She said it was only my dad.

My mum is in love with a curious man
And it seems that at last I know who:
My dad left those letters.
If I knew him better
Then maybe I'd love my dad too.

Not A Care In The World

I worry a lot.
In school we watched a programme
about the Great Plague,
and for the next few nights all I could see
were bodies, contorted and diseased
at the foot of my bed.

We talked about the Second World War,
and I worried about what I would do
if there was a war now – whether I'd be dead
and whether or not my family would survive.
I asked my mum if she was ever alive
during a war, and she said yes, of course –
there are wars going on
across the world all the time.
But what about in England? I asked.
She said she remembered the Falklands War,
which wasn't *in* England but did
involve our army.

I worry a lot.
I worry about being poor
and about famine.
On television I saw an advert
asking people to donate money
to another country
where there wasn't enough to eat.

The people in the advert were covered in sheets.
They looked like barren winter trees.
I wondered whether my mum would be able to
  love me
if I looked like that, and whether
I'd be able to love her if she did.
I've started hoarding cans of food under my bed,
in case there's a famine in London.

I worry a lot.
And it isn't just big things I worry about either;
I also worry about lots and lots and lots and lots
of little things.
We had some maths homework
I didn't understand, which I worried about
until I cried over the breakfast table.
And last week I tried to write a book review
on a book I haven't even read.
I'm worried that my teacher will find out
and make me read the whole thing,
maybe even twice.
And whenever we have to get into pairs
to go on a school trip
I worry myself sick
about who I'm going to stand next to.
Sam likes girls now
so he always wants to hold a girl's hand.
James and Alex usually stand together.

So now we're on a trip and my heart
is a hammer in my chest. We're standing
in the line, two abreast –
I've been worrying about this for weeks.
The birds of anxiety peck at me with their beaks
as two old ladies pass us on the street,
eyeing us as though
they want to pinch our cheeks.
Then one turns to the other and says

"It must be great being a kid, mustn't it?
Not a care in the world."

Let's Play!

(Read this as quickly as you can!)

Let's play...

[deep breath]

Goodies and baddies
and mummies and daddies
and doctors and nurses
and writers of verses
and cops and then robbers
and robbers and cops
and let's skip and let's jump
and let's run and let's hop
and let's go wild
and let's play dead
and let's crack eggs
and let's bake bread
and let's play goats
and let's play sheep
and let's go upstairs
and go off to sleep.

write your own poem

write your own poem

write your own poem

write your own poem

write your own poem

write your own poem

write your own poem